Phonicability Games

VERA CONWAY

THREE-LETTER WORDS

l eg

b ed

h at

d

z

Phonicability Games

CONTENTS

Published by Hopscotch Educational Publishing Ltd,
29 Waterloo Place, Leamington Spa CV32 5LA.
(Tel: 01926 744227)

© 2000 Hopscotch Educational Publishing

Written by Vera Conway
Series design by Blade Communications
Illustrated by Jean de Lemos and Tony O'Donnell
Printed by Clintplan, Southam

ISBN 1-902239-48-2

Introduction

The idea of inventing games of this nature was first conceived out of sheer desperation when I met my first uncooperative pupil. He told me confidently "I do not need to learn to read because I am going to be an actor." As he was then only seven years old and quite unable to project his mind into the future, no argument of mine could convince him to believe otherwise.

A year later when this boy was diagnosed as being severely dyslexic he was triumphant. He stubbornly closed his mind to everyone's attempts to help him and his behaviour in school gave much cause for concern, but our lessons continued. I spent two hours with him each week and, in spite of himself, he learned to read and write. The almost-miracle was achieved by means of games we played together, which he actually enjoyed.

Since then, every game in this series has been played time and time again with pupils who have a variety of problems as well as with those who appear to learn to read and write without experiencing any difficulties. As I saw more and more pupils benefiting from playing the games, I wanted to share them with other pupils – both old and young – so that they could experience the joy and laughter that comes with learning to read and spell. I hope, also, that school teachers, parent teachers and helpers of all kinds will become better acquainted with the simple logic of teaching reading and spelling by phonics (sounds).

This is by no means a return to something old fashioned in a back-to-basics approach. We are all discovering the real worth of a teaching method which, speaking generally, has not been profoundly comprehended. Nor has it been widely appreciated, so the subject could not have been taught effectively in the past. Fortunately, things are changing now; the extensive illiteracy throughout English speaking countries has excited much research. This adds authenticity to many small, enlightening experiments and discoveries currently being made by the few teachers who have the courage to probe. We are finding not only that it is pleasurable to teach reading and spelling by phonics, but also that hardly any pupils need to fail to learn to read.

I use these games in conjunction with Mrs Violet Brand's scheme, using the order in which the sounds are introduced in *Fat Sam* (Egon). Each game supports and extends the new steps within the structure of the scheme, but they can be played in any order.

The games are unbelievably simple and, in principle, well within the capabilities of every potential reader, from the youngest beginners to older pupils who may be experiencing difficulties. Currently, my youngest pupil is five and the oldest is 57! One of my pupils, who was 14 when I first played the games with her, was so impressed by their efficacy that she is now studying child care and working with young children and is designing and making games of her own to help them.

Each game either practises and reinforces the sound/symbol relationship which has just been taught or introduces the pupil to the next one. Some games combine these two aims. When the games are presented to the pupil at the optimum moments in her reading development, newly learned rules are established. (NB. We have used 'she' throughout this book to refer to the pupil. This is done purely for the purposes of consistency and clarity. It is not intended to imply that females have more problems with reading than males. In other books in the series we shall use 'he' throughout.)

Although these games can help any pupil to learn to read and spell, they have proved to be particularly useful and effective for pupils who have experienced years of failure in most of their school subjects because of their poor reading skills. One eight-year-old boy who was sent to me to receive 'help' draped himself over the back of his chair as we began the first lesson and refused to look at anything on the table. Learning to read had become anathema to him; he had received plenty of 'help', but he still couldn't read and so he had given up trying. His reaction presented a tense moment for me; I did not know the child and I certainly did not want to spoil our relationship before it had even begun! I took out a game and shook the dice. "Look Perry," I said. "I am playing a game, and I am winning." Fortunately, he won… and gladly came again.

Success in winning the games does not depend on a pupil's ability to read or spell. The real secret of success lies in the fact that, quite subtly, the learning/teaching element is relegated to second place in favour of 'luck'. Because of this, pupils do not feel anxious when they play. There are no worries or tensions; they are confident that they **can** tackle something that appears to be so easy. In such a relaxed atmosphere, they can enjoy the fun of playing and even the triumph of beating the teacher! This latter achievement boosts the confidence of almost every pupil and it is very important to them. I have heard little ones discussing the play later in the day and looking very pleased with themselves as they've said, "I won two games today."

On the other hand, if the pupil loses, she can experience losing a game respectably, without any sense of failure, since she knows that she lost because the dice did not fall in her favour and definitely not because she was stupid!

Teachers will not, of course, be trying to win! On the contrary, and especially with younger pupils or those whose confidence needs to be built up, the teacher will contrive to lose the game! They will soon learn subtle ways to lose, by forgetting where the winning card is, by missing a turn, by always allowing the pupil to go first at the beginning of play, by working out whose will be the last card and by making helpful suggestions to the pupil so that he gets the advantage. I have also even turned a blind eye to a little cheating that works towards my purpose. Pupils have to know what they are doing in order to cheat… but of course I make it very clear that I do not approve of cheating and I correct it when I 'see' it!

Each game has its own very clear aim about which part of the reading structure it supports. There are, however, some subsidiary aims which make the games even more valuable; look out for these as you play.

ASSESSMENT

This is sometimes, for me, the main reason for playing a game. I often need to assess how much of the new work the pupil has assimilated and whether or not she is ready to go on. I assess the situation continually as I watch her strategies as she plays the game. I 'listen' to her thinking processes and to the use she makes of the sounds in the words. I need to know if she is really hearing the sounds or travelling down the dead-end road of remembering the words in 'look and say' fashion. If the latter is true, I know that more practice, more patient explanation and more adaptation to approach the problem from a different angle are all needed. During every game, I have to learn when to wait patiently for the pupil to remember and when to intervene with reassuring help. Playing these games has, in fact, helped me to be able to assess more precisely where my pupil is in her progress and how to help her move on.

VOCABULARY

Each of these games extends the pupils' spoken vocabulary as well as helping them to read and spell. I always talk to them about the words we are using, about the meanings of the words and how they fit into sentences. I have been surprised by the number of pupils who do not know how to use some of the simple, three-letter words such as 'tub', 'wig', 'den', 'fig' and 'pan', let alone the more difficult ones. I encourage the pupils to give clear definitions of the words to help them to remember when they later need to read them and use them in their own compositions.

MEMORY TRAINING

Memory training is intrinsic to many of the games and with some ingenuity on the part of the teacher even more use can be made of the games to help pupils remember than might at first be apparent. I often ask questions while we are playing, such as "Where is the elephant?" or "Is the stork under the 'ar' or the 'or'?" The most difficult part of learning to spell is remembering which symbol to use from the selection which represent the same sound: 'ai', 'ay', 'a-e' for example. Should 'rain' be spelled 'rane', 'rayne' or 'rain'? The games most certainly help to sort out problems of this kind.

As you become more familiar with the games, countless opportunities will occur to you for using the materials to test pupils' memory skills.

CONCLUSION

It has been my intention to make the games simple, attractive and fun to play. I have borne in mind, too, that they need to be played in a short time because I know from experience how little time many teachers have to spend with individual pupils.

I hope that the games can be photocopied cheaply so that copies may be taken home. Young children especially like to share what they have enjoyed with their families and the additional practice will be good for them. Alternatively, sets of games can be made up and stored as a resource, which can be lent to parents and returned.

The clear aims and simple rules help parents to become effective teachers who, in turn, can give valuable help in playing the games with other pupils. The components of the games may also be used as a resource to illustrate specific teaching points. I have used the games in this way with older pupils who do not necessarily need the competitive approach.

The pictures will also inspire many useful worksheets and ideas for new games, so there are many uses for these photocopiable materials.

PLAYING THE GAMES

Most of the games are designed for two players who can either be the pupil and the teacher or two pupils playing together with the teacher or competent adult as referee. All reading games need supervision and mine are no exception, but the simplicity of these enables parents and classroom helpers to grasp the principles quickly to support the work of the teacher.

The rules of these games are very flexible and can be modified by the teacher to suit the pupil. Pupils sometimes change the rules and I have been happy to allow them to do that provided that the game is still fair and the main aims are accomplished.

There is a great deal of repetition of the rules across the selection of games. This aids each pupil's confidence and allows them to concentrate on the main purpose of the game without having to contend with more complicated instructions.

Pupils should move through the scheme at their own pace and teachers will find that there are more games for those sound/symbol groups which need most practice. Not all pupils need to play all of the games. Teachers need to be aware of individual pupil's needs. There is little to be gained from playing a game once a pupil has understood that step, except, perhaps, to boost his confidence.

Teachers and helpers need to make sure that pupils know what the pictures represent before the game begins. Such a preview lends opportunity to talk about words and pictures and is an important part of the learning process.

HOW TO MAKE THE GAMES

○ Photocopy the required pages according to the instructions for each game, enlarging or reducing, as you prefer. I made all my games to fit into zipped reading book folders measuring 40 x 27cms. This helps to keep the weight down when I have to carry a selection of games to school.

○ Colour the pictures; I have found coloured pencils to be the best tools to use. Enlist the help of anyone who is willing, but if you intend to make your games permanent, make sure that your 'colourers' have high standards.

○ Cut up the sheets as instructed and mount the pieces and the boards on card using an adhesive.

○ If you intend to cover your games with Tacky Back, (and this will certainly preserve them for much use in the future) then use water-based ink pens. Spirit based ink spreads under Tacky Back. You may prefer to mount the games on thinner card and laminate them.

EXTRA EQUIPMENT REQUIRED

○ Nearly all of the games can be played in a shorter time, if necessary, so I find it useful to carry an egg timer in my bag.

○ Blank dice can be obtained from:-
Taskmaster Ltd, Morris Road, Leicester LE2 6BR

○ Make your feely bags from attractive pieces of material. Cut out a rectangle which is just a little longer than an A4 sheet of paper. Stitch the sides and hem the top. Thread a string through if you wish.

○ Buttons can be used for counters, or you can buy some from Taskmaster (see above). For 'counters' to move on the board, I collect trinkets or small toys from cereal packets. All these little novelties help to make the games more attractive.

○ Stock up with zipped reading book folders for simple storage. I label my folders with my own description of the contents so that I can find the game I need quickly. I also put a mounted copy of the rules for the game into the folder with the pieces.

○ Patience! – You will need much patience too. If you have a will to teach reading, patience grows with the thrill of achievement in both pupil and teacher. I trust that these little games will bring much satisfaction to many people.

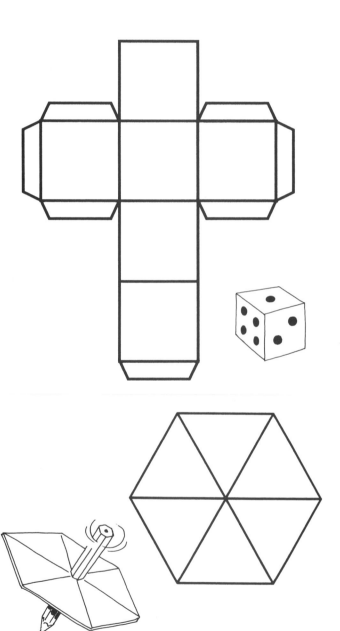

An emergency dice or spinner can be made using the pattern opposite. You can enlarge or reduce it according to your needs.

Using this book

Once letter sounds and their symbols have been understood, pupils will be ready to blend the sounds into words for themselves and to recognise (read) words with those sounds in them.

Anyone can put ingredients into a bowl, but it takes special care to blend those ingredients into a delicious meal. So it is with phonics. The blending is all important. The adult has to demonstrate to the pupil how to allow the sounds to emerge gently, in succession, in the right order, without adding any other 'rogue' sounds which require an unwanted change in the position of the lips, tongue or teeth.

For example
mmmm aaa nnnn (man) and not **muh an ner**

The games in this book will help with problems that often arise. Some pupils find it difficult to hear the last letter in a word and many take more time to identify the vowels. Be patient – don't give up!

Initial Sounds Games

AIMS

- ⃝ To give pupils practice in hearing the first sound of a word.
- ⃝ To give the adult opportunity to demonstrate word building.

HOW TO MAKE THE GAMES

- ⃝ Cut out the picture cards, then cut off the first letter from each picture card. Pages 9 and 15 are the letter trays.
- ⃝ There are two similar games to be played with these cards. The first uses consonants from b to l and the second from m to z.

WHAT YOU NEED

- ⃝ A dice with 's' for 'stop' on one side and 'g' for 'go' on five sides but one 'g' should be written in red.

- ⃝ A shaking cup.

HOW TO PLAY

Two pupils or more can play with the adult guiding them. Alternatively this game can be played with the adult and one pupil.

- ⃝ The pupil should first match the letter cards to the letter tray, with the adult helping to sound them as they are placed. Then stack the picture cards.

- ⃝ The players have turns to throw the dice. If 'g' is thrown, this means that she can go. She takes a picture card from the stack, find its initial letter and sets the completed word aside. If a red 'g' is thrown, the player may complete two words, but if 's' for 'stop' is thrown, she must miss one turn.

- ⃝ When all the cards have been used up, the player with the most completed word cards is the winner.

TEACHER GUIDANCE

As you prepare to play this game, remind the pupil that you are putting the letters that stand for the first sounds on the tray. Practise producing these sounds together, linking them with a word from the game. You might say, "Here is 'b'." (say the sound), or you may say, "Here is 'bee'." (the letter name) It stands for 'b' (say the sound) and we need it when we say 'bag'."

Remember that when you say the first sound, you have to get your mouth ready to say the word and then allow the tiny sound to emerge. Be careful to add nothing extra. Do not make it into 'buh' or 'ber' because 'ber–ag–ger' does not say 'bag'.

When you play this game, you have the opportunity to demonstrate how the three sounds uttered in succession make the word. Do this frequently and casually, but do not spoil the game by being boring!

Your pupil might grasp the principle of three-letter-word building from this game, but she needs to be able to spell the words as well as to read them, so do not jump to any premature conclusions.

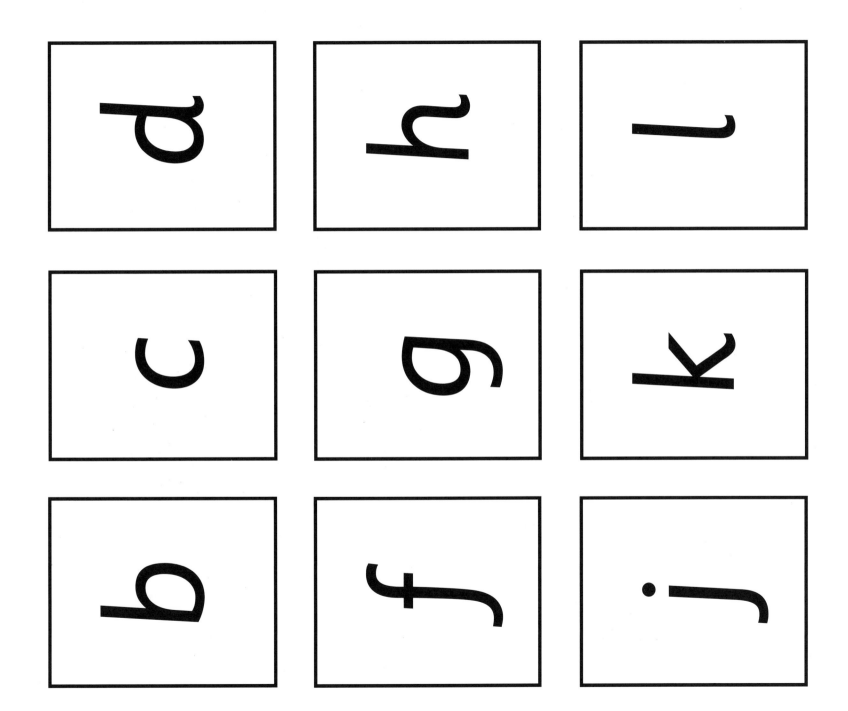

eg	**id**	**ig**	**ed**
l	**k**	**d**	**b**

h en	h at	j am	g um

l id

l ip

d og

h ot

us

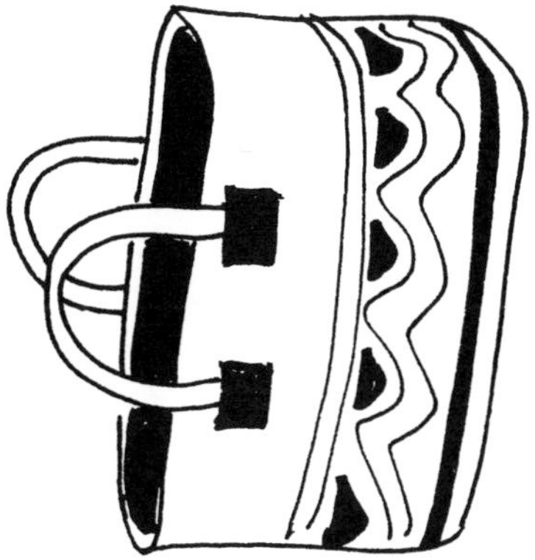

ag

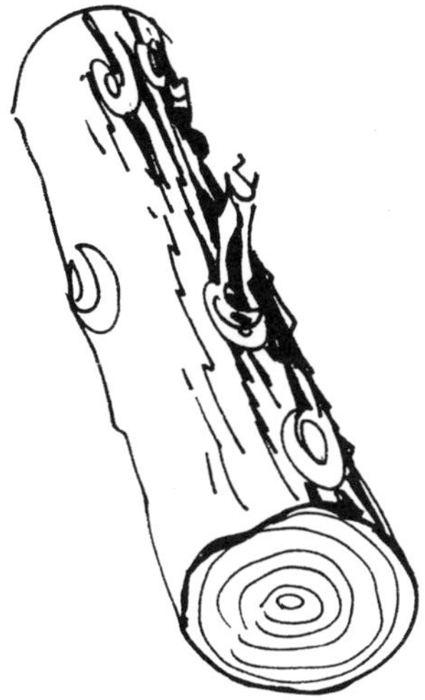

og

ot

b

b

l

c

an	ox	up	ug
f	f	c	j

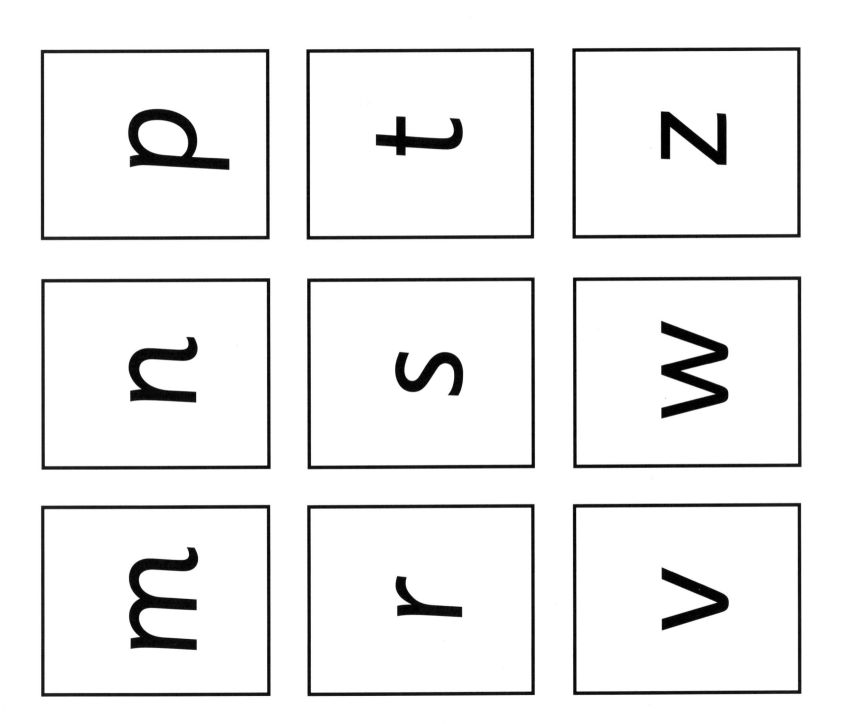

			10
eg	ot	en	en
p	p	m	t

ug	ub	un	et
m	t	s	n

ap	at	en	op
m	m	p	m

v an	r at	p an	m ud

	ip	z
	ig	p
	ix	s
	eb	w

The Consonant-Plus-Vowel Game

AIMS

❍ To stress the first consonant plus vowel blend in simple words.

❍ To help the pupil to hear the blend and to add the final sound.

HOW TO MAKE THE GAME

❍ Cut up the cards and cut off the last letter, as indicated.

HOW TO PLAY

❍ Each player is dealt three picture cards and the rest are stacked.

❍ The letter cards are placed face down in neat rows on the table.

❍ Players take turns to select a letter card and to match it with one of their picture cards. If a match is possible, the completed word is set aside and the player takes a new picture card from the stack. If the letter card does not match, it must be put back.

❍ When there are no picture cards left, the first player to complete all of his last three words stops the game and both players count their word cards. The player with the most is the winner.

TEACHER GUIDANCE

Educationists have puzzled for some time over whether to teach 'ca... t' or 'c ... at'. The danger is that 'ca' or 'at' could be presented as sound pictures and they are not – 'c' is one sound picture, 'a' another and 't' another, because their sounds are not altered by being together. (In the case of 'sh' the sounds are not heard separately, as 's' and 'h' but are together – a picture of a new sound.)

Give your pupil some independence. Listen to her sounding out and help when she needs you. Watch the way she works – pupils do not always sound out aloud, but you are waiting for her to go for the right letter unhesitatingly.

$\frac{2+}{2}$ $\frac{2}{4}$	su	m	le	g
do g		g	be	d
10	te	n	ca	t
di		g		

PHONICABILITY THREE-LETTER WORDS

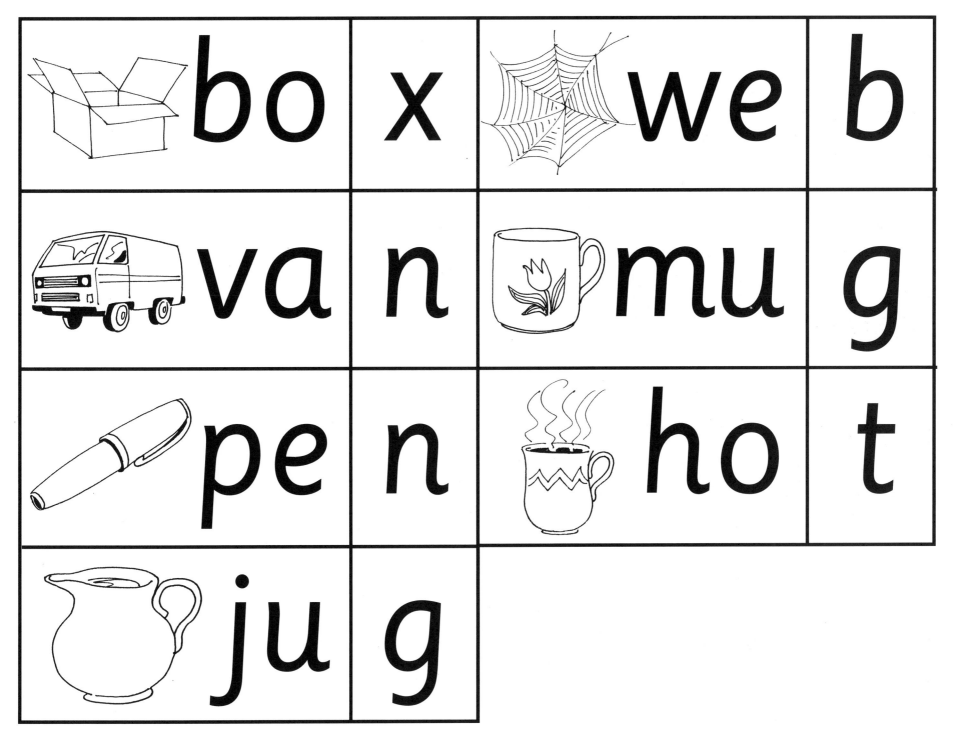

bo	x	we	b
va	n	mu	g
pe	n	ho	t
ju	g		

23

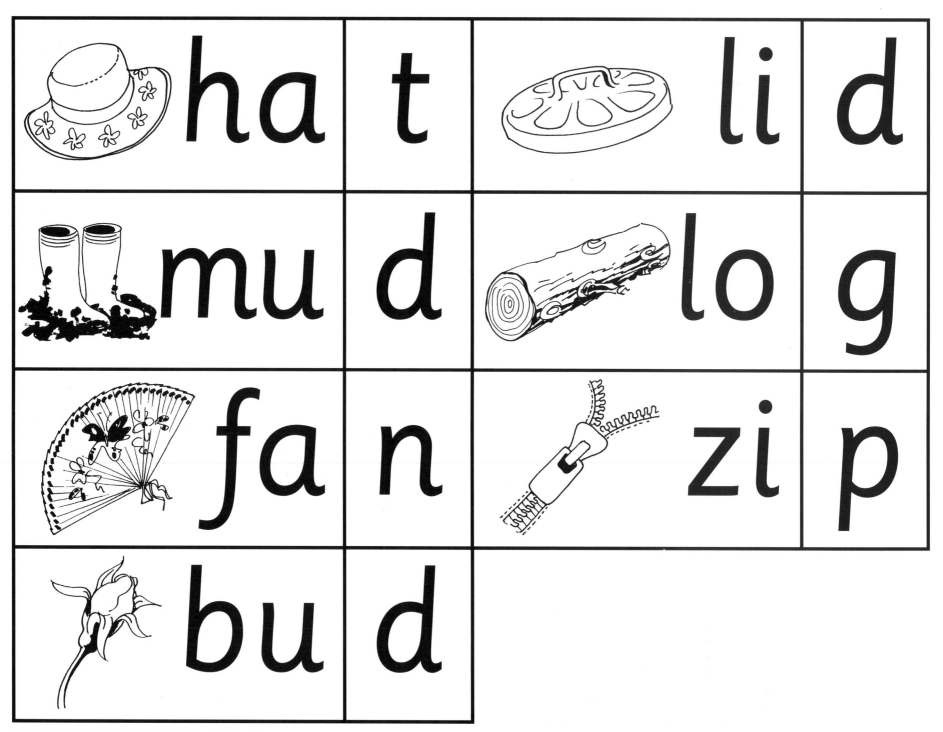

ha	t	li	d
mu	d	lo	g
fa	n	zi	p
bu	d		

24

The Last sound Game

AIMS

○ To stress the final sound in a word.

○ To give pupils practice in hearing and visualising the first two sounds in simple words.

○ To give practice in word building.

HOW TO MAKE THE GAME

○ Cut up the cards and cut off the first two letters as indicated.

HOW TO PLAY

○ Deal three picture cards to each player then stack the remaining cards.

○ Place the small letter cards in neat rows, face down on the table.

○ Players take turns to select a letter card and try to pair it with one of their picture cards. If it can be paired, the completed word is set aside and another picture card is taken. If the letter card cannot be matched to a picture card it must be returned to the stack.

○ When all the cards have been used up, the winner is the player with the most completed words.

TEACHER GUIDANCE

Some pupils experience difficulty in hearing the last sound in any three-letter word. Before you play the game, listen to the words as you say them and check that you are saying the last sound. We sometimes speak in a lazy way and say things like, "He's go' a ca'." (He's got a cat.) and the tongue never gets into position behind the top teeth to say that 't' sound properly.

Help the pupil to hear that last sound, then sound out the whole word carefully, helping him to hear each sound separately. You are working on word building by sequencing the separate sounds in words and this is absolutely the foundation to learning to read and spell.

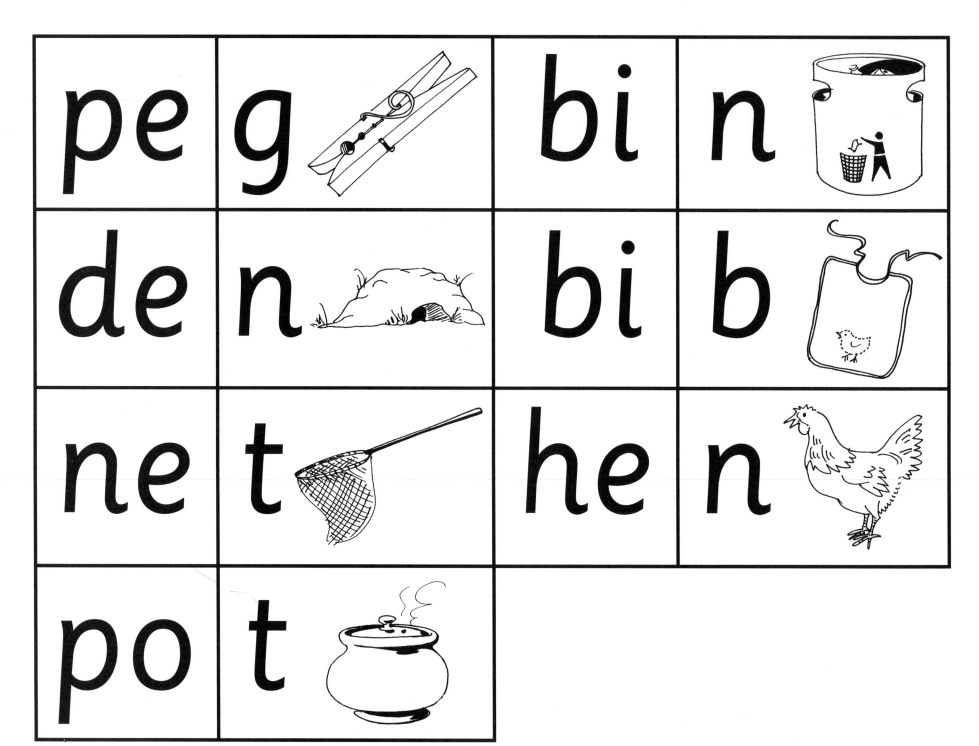

pe g	bi n
de n	bi b
ne t	he n
po t	

PHONICABILITY **THREE-LETTER WORDS**

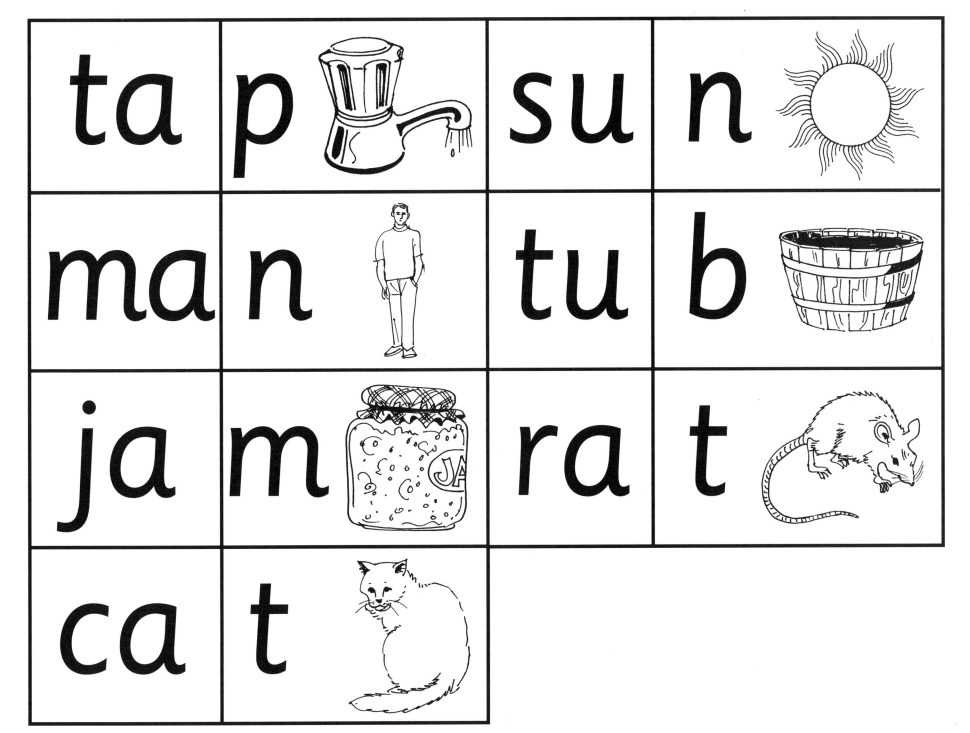

fo	x	bun	
mo	p	ki	d
cu	p	pi	g
co	t		

PHONICABILITY THREE-LETTER WORDS

Word and Picture Matching
Vowel sound 'a'

AIMS

○ To give practice to pupils who have learned to build three-letter words using the vowel 'a'.

HOW TO MAKE THE GAME

○ The picture sheets are the boards. Cut up the word cards.

HOW TO PLAY

○ Place all the word cards neatly, word side down, on the table.

○ The players take turns to select a word card, read it and place it correctly on their board if they have the picture to match it. If not, then the word card is returned to its place.

○ The winner's board is the one completed first.

TEACHER GUIDANCE

This is essentially a reading game and young pupils particularly are very proud of themselves when they have won. They have to sound out and read the words all by themselves.

I usually play this game after we have looked at a number of words containing the vowel sound 'a' and sounded them out. The pupil is ready to play this game when she understands the principle of blending. Give help if it is needed, quietly, without making her feel a failure, but if she needs a lot of help, then you should do a lot more work on word building – and stay with vowel 'a' lists until she has grasped the principle.

pan	van	cap	bag
map	cat	fan	can
tap	mat	bat	
rat	jam	hat	

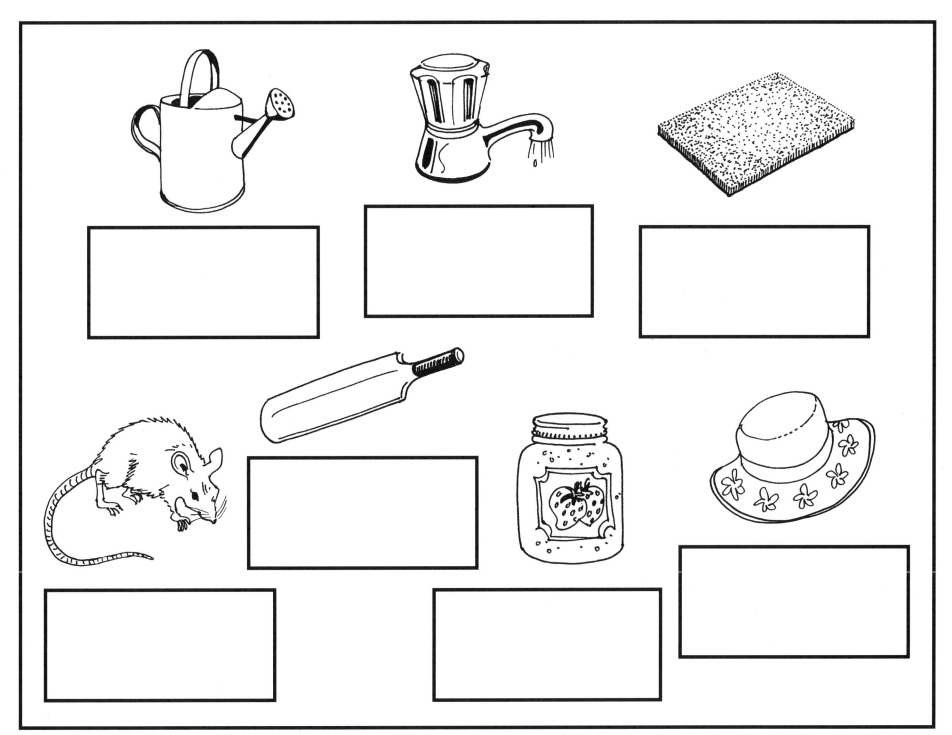

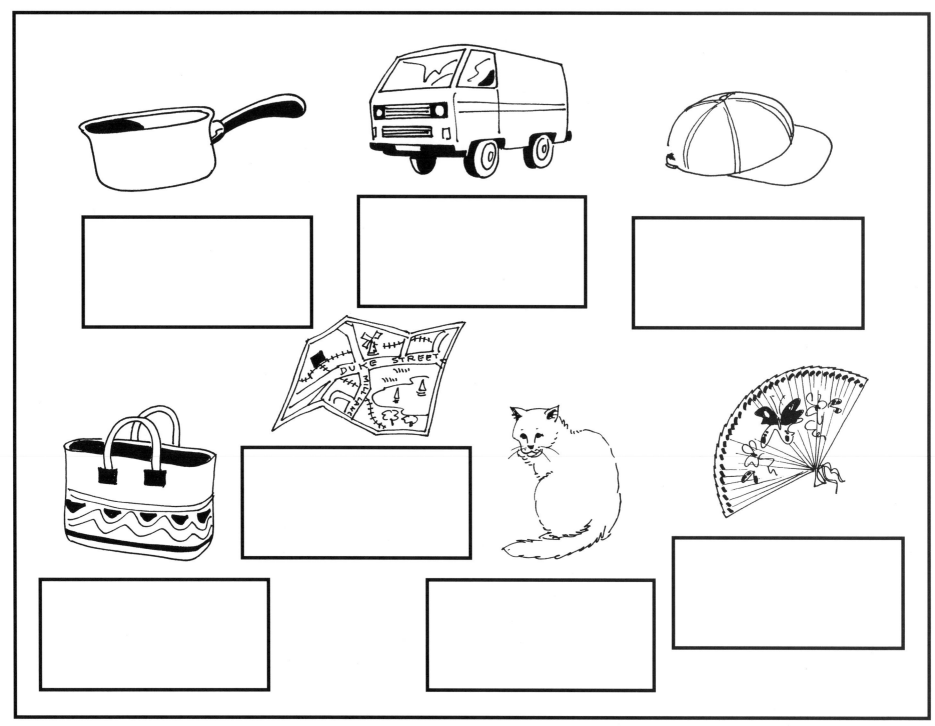

Word and Picture Matching
Vowel sounds 'i' and 'o'

AIMS

○ To give pupils who have learned to build three-letter words extra practice in recognising words containing the vowel sounds 'i' and 'o'.

HOW TO MAKE THE GAME

○ The four sheets are two pairs: page 34 matches with page 35, and page 36 with page 37. One sheet of each pair forms the baseboard and the other is cut into playing cards of words and pictures.

WHAT YOU NEED

○ A shaking cup and a dice with three sides marked 'i' and the other three marked 'o'.

HOW TO PLAY

○ Players choose a board each and take turns to throw the dice.

○ The small cards are placed neatly, face up, on the table.

○ The player who throws an 'i' must select a picture or a word card with that sound in it to match with one of the pictures or words on his board. Likewise for 'o'. The winner fills his board first.

TEACHER GUIDANCE

This is a reading game and I do not play it until the pupil has understood how to sound out words containing 'a' confidently and has done some work on 'i' and 'o'. My pupils have usually taken home their lists of 'i' words and 'o' words to practise with, so I expect certain success when we play this simple game.

Give the pupils a little help when it is needed. Be prepared for the need to be quiet and still while the pupil concentrates. I encourage them to think carefully because a careless glance often results in the confusion and misreading of words that are in some way similar, such as 'lip' and 'lid'.

bib

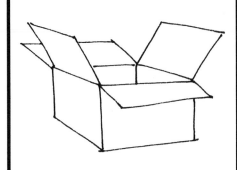

lid

six

lip

kid

rod

box

pig

6

bin

cot

mop

doll

dig

tin

fox

pot

log

pin   hot

 zip

dog  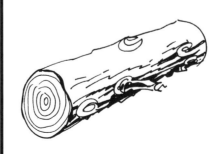 wig

Word and Picture Matching
Vowel sounds 'u' and 'e'

AIMS

○ To give practice to pupils who have learned to build three-letter words using the vowel sounds 'u' and 'e'.

HOW TO MAKE THE GAME

○ The picture sheets are the boards. Cut up the word cards.

HOW TO PLAY

○ The players choose a board each.

○ Place the word cards neatly, face down on the table.

○ The players take turns to select a word card and match it, if they can, with a picture on their board. If the card cannot be matched, it should be returned to the pool. The winner's board is filled first.

○ Alternatively, the word sheets may be used for boards and pictures cut up and mounted, to give additional reading practice, as required.

TEACHER GUIDANCE

This reading game gives continued practice in sounding out words and matching them with their pictures. Do not play it until you feel that the pupil knows how to tackle it. Competent reading in this game does not necessarily mean competent spelling, so you will need to test that too. If the pupil can read these words she will soon be ready to move on to four-letter words.

Listen to make sure that the sounding out runs smoothly and is not interrupted by rogue sounds, 'mer' and 'ner' for instance. Now is the time to correct such mispronunciation. Ask the pupil to say the sounds again, properly, after you. We only want 'mmm–a–nnn'.

Try to get the pupil to do all the sounding out. It is best if she can do this independently and it will help you to assess her understanding of word building so far.

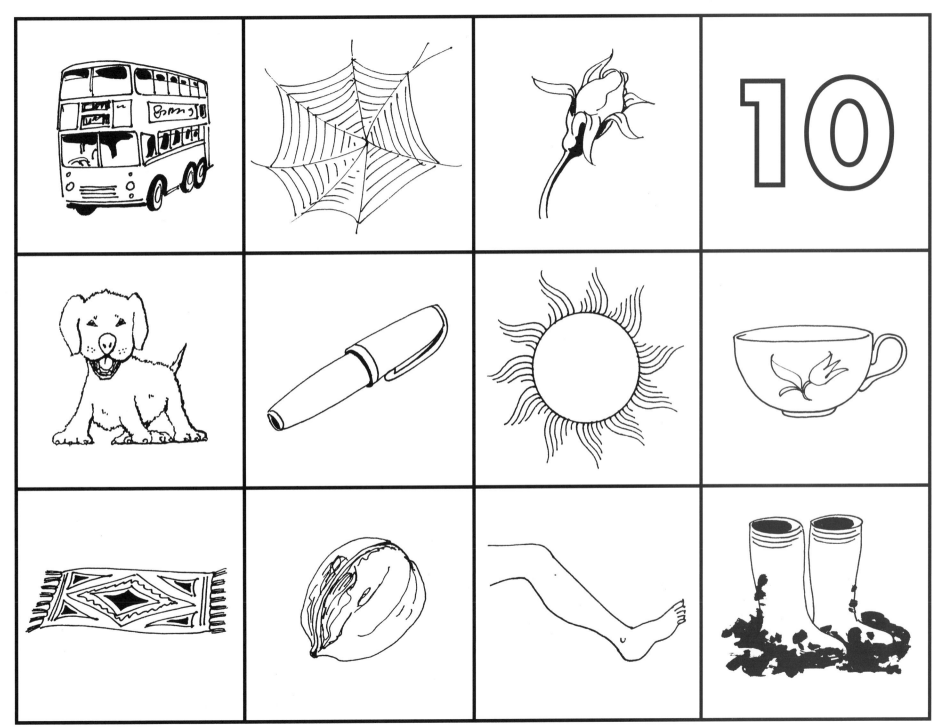

bus	web	bud	ten
pup	pen	sun	cup
rug	nut	leg	mud

vet	peg	mug	sum
tub	hen	bun	men
bed	jug	net	gum

The 'e' and 'i' Fishing Game

AIMS

○ To help pupils to distinguish between the sounds 'e' and 'i'.

HOW TO MAKE THE GAME

○ Cut up all the cards and stick the fish on the reverse sides of the picture cards with words and pictures matching.

WHAT YOU NEED

○ A dice which has 'e' on two of its sides, 'i 'on two sides and red spots on the remaining sides.

○ A shaking cup.

HOW TO PLAY

○ The cards are placed neatly, picture side up, on the table.

○ Players take turns to throw the dice. If 'e' is thrown, that player may choose a picture which has the sound 'e' in its word. Likewise for 'i'.

○ If a red spot is thrown, the player must miss a turn.

○ The winning player catches the most fish.

TEACHER GUIDANCE

However diligent you are, many pupils confuse the sounds of 'e' and 'i'. I have found that a misunderstanding of vowel sounds has been a stumbling block to the reading development of many pupils. How can anyone read anything if they do not know accurately what the letters 'a', 'e', 'i', 'o' and 'u' stand for?

When you play this game, help the pupil to hear the subtle difference between 'i' and 'e'. Be patient and wait for her to try out the words in her mouth. Encourage her to leave the word on the table until she is sure of picking up the right one. Pupils develop a clever knack of looking at my face to see if they are right or wrong. They will do that to you, too – but make sure that they do the thinking and reserve your smile of encouragement for the times when they choose the right sound.

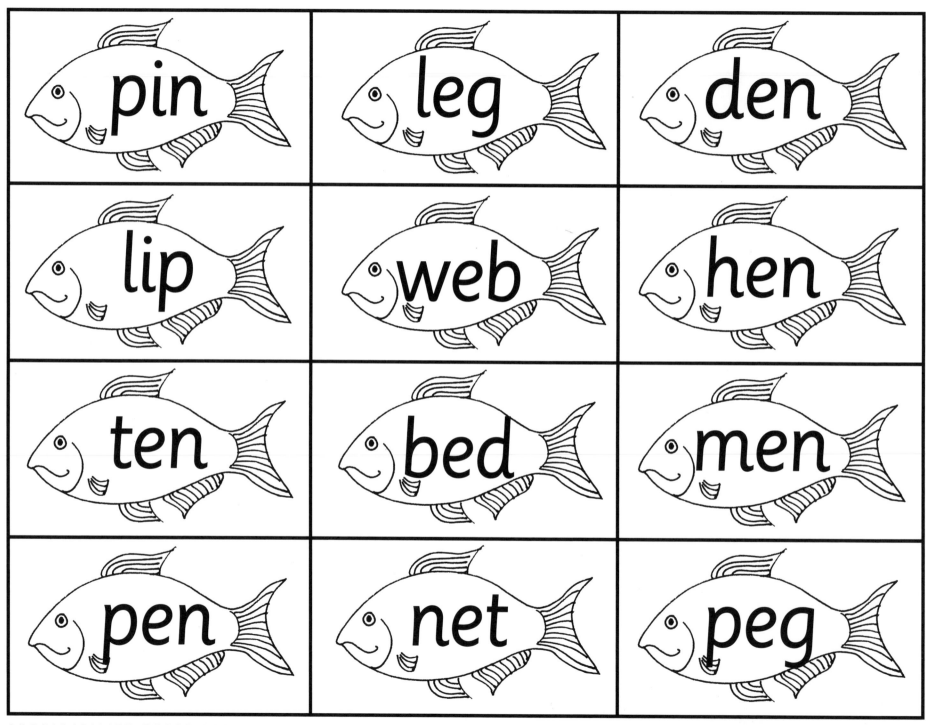

PHONICABILITY THREE-LETTER WORDS

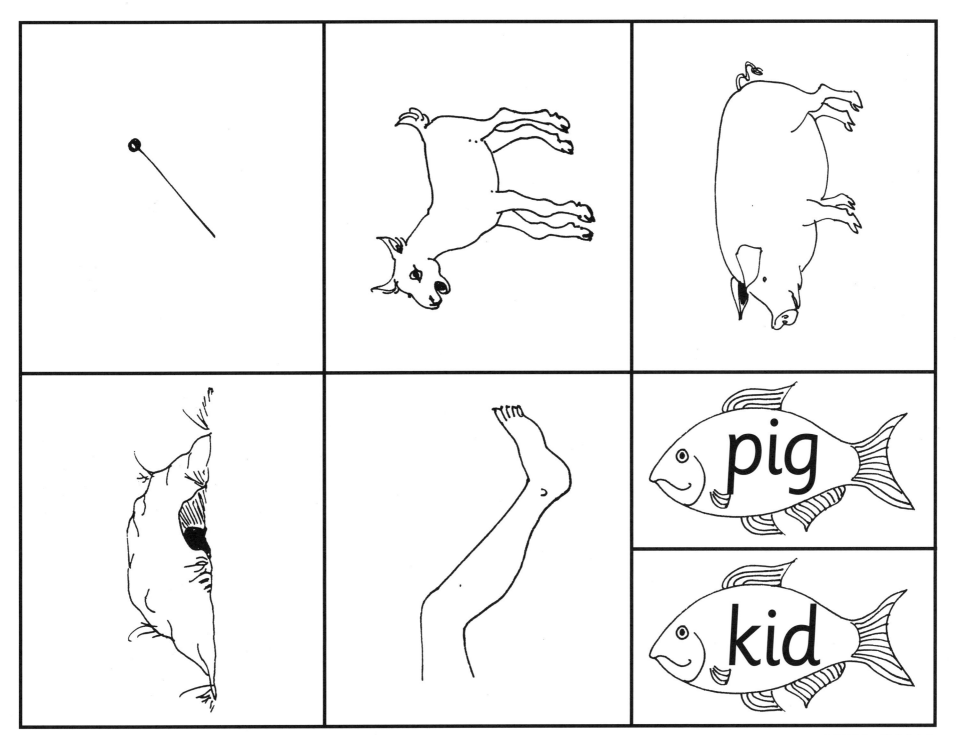

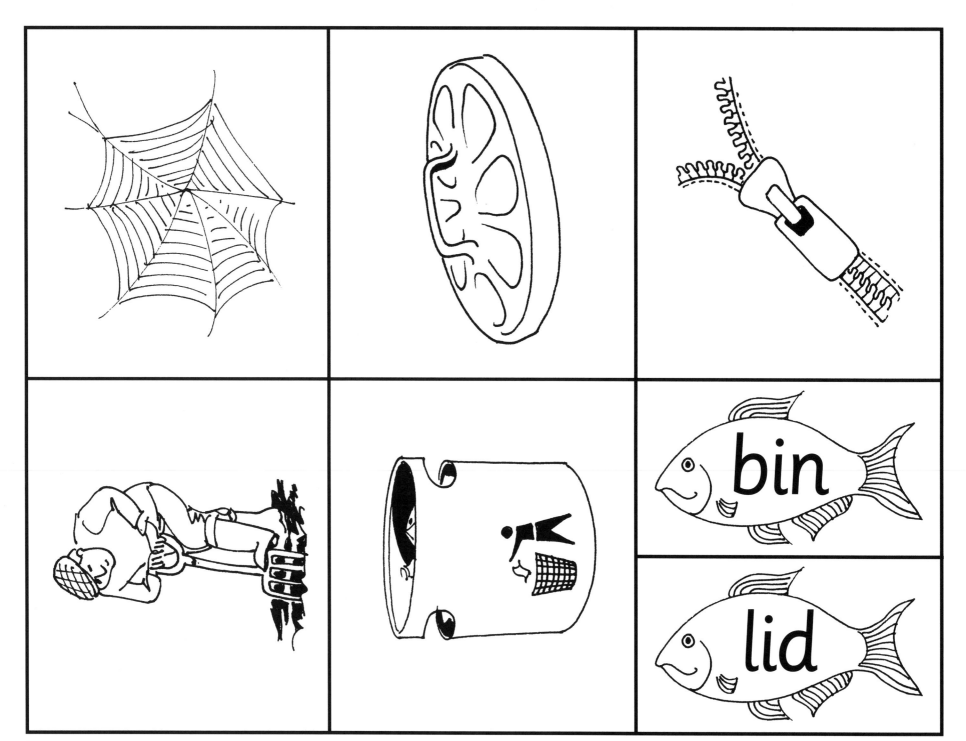

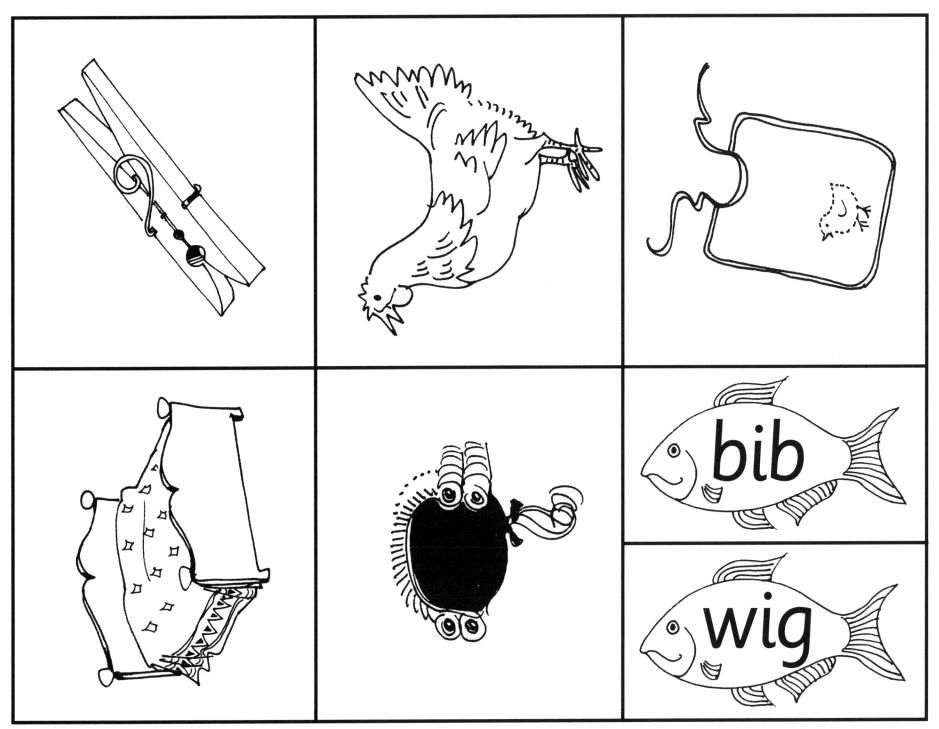

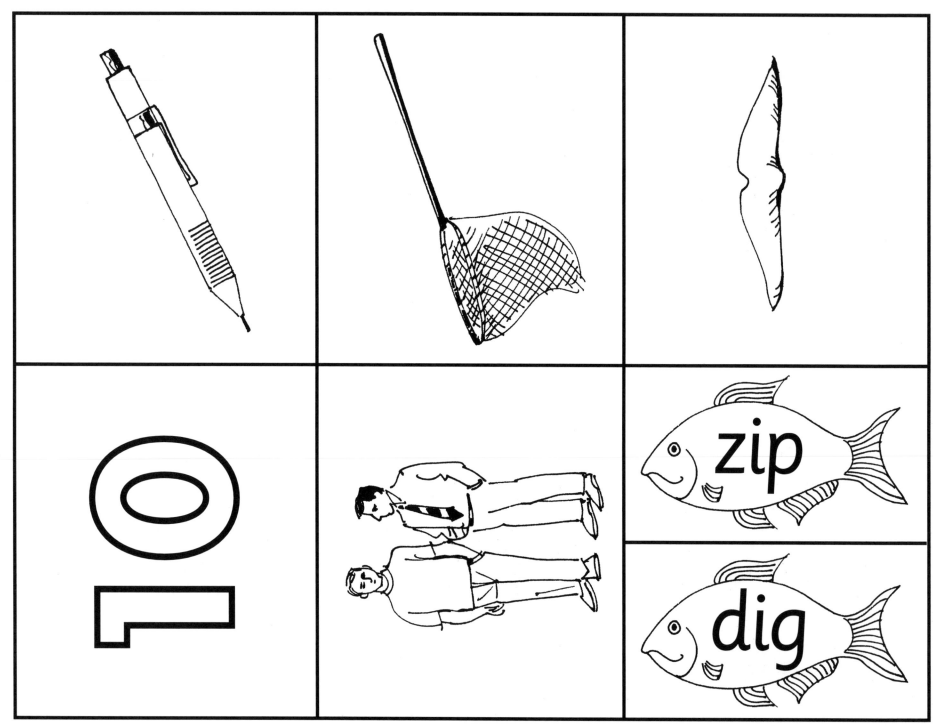

PHONICABILITY THREE-LETTER WORDS

Missing Middles

AIMS

MISSING MIDDLES 1

○ To give pupils practice in hearing and supplying the vowel sound in three-letter words.

MISSING MIDDLES 2

○ To give the pupils practice in hearing the vowel sound in simple three-letter words.

MISSING MIDDLES 3

○ To give pupils practice in hearing and supplying the vowel sound in three-letter words.

MISSING MIDDLES 4

○ To give the pupils practice in hearing the vowel sound in simple three-letter words.

MISSING MIDDLES 1

HOW TO MAKE THE GAME

○ The picture sheets are the boards. Cut up all the small vowel cards and place them in a feely bag.

WHAT YOU NEED

○ One feely bag.

HOW TO PLAY

○ Players choose one board each and take turns to dip into the bag. (Players who can cope may use two boards.)

○ If the vowel drawn out from the bag fills one of the words on the player's board, he may keep it; if not, it must be returned to the bag.

○ The player to fill her board first is the winner.

TEACHER GUIDANCE

Correct pronunciation of vowel sounds is very important for reading, but especially for spelling. I (partly) solved the problem of how to give the pupils extensive experience in sounding and using the vowels in three-letter words by making these 'missing middles' games. Teachers should practise saying the sounds for themselves so that they do not make the mistakes that their pupils make of fudging 'e' and 'i' and 'o' and 'u'. Help the pupil to sound the whole word as she places the vowel. If she puts a vowel into the wrong word, help her to read what she has made so that she understands her mistake. Help her to put it right and smile about it!

MISSING MIDDLES 2

HOW TO MAKE THE GAME

○ The picture sheets are the boards. Cut up the word cards on pages 55 and 56.

HOW TO PLAY

This game may be played with a group of four players plus a leader.

○ The word cards are shuffled and stacked.

○ Players choose one board each (or two each if only two are playing).

○ The leader reads the word on one of the word cards and the players look to see if they have the appropriate picture.

○ The player who has the picture named can have the card if she can say the sound of the missing vowel.

○ The first player to fill his board is the winner. (I have always helped players who could not supply the right sound, but should it appear fairer not to help, then the word card should be tucked back into the stack, not placed at the bottom.)

TEACHER GUIDANCE

Play this game when the pupils are able to sound out three-letter words but need more practice to get the vowel right.

When you read the word card, you may feel that it is helpful for some pupils if you sound out the word before saying it – "p...o...t, pot".

Missing Middles

On another occasion, you could try just sounding out the word and allowing the pupils to hear the whole. The pupil must give you the sound of the missing letter. If she names it, you will need to ask "What does 'oh' stand for?" and then repeat the sounding out of the whole word.

This game lends itself to group play because all the pupils are involved at the same time. Pupils up to the age of eight are impatient for their turn if they are expected to play in groups and many lose interest.

MISSING MIDDLES 3

HOW TO MAKE THE GAME

○ Cut up all the picture cards. Stick the appropriate vowel on the reverse of each picture.

WHAT YOU NEED

○ A dice with 'a', 'e', 'i', 'o', 'u' and a red spot on the sixth side.

○ A shaking cup.

○ An egg timer if the lesson time is limited.

HOW TO PLAY

○ Place all the picture cards neatly on the table with the picture side facing upwards.

○ Players take turns to throw the dice. According to which vowel is thrown, they must select a picture with the sound in its word. If a red spot is thrown, that player must miss a turn.

○ The game continues until all the cards are used up, or until the time runs out.

○ The player with the most cards is the winner.

TEACHER GUIDANCE

This is a 'listening game' to give the pupils practice in listening to the sounds in the word and extracting the middle one. It is not easy because the pupil has a lot of pictures in front of her to 'listen' to. Be patient. Give her time to work out the problem.

I played this game with a four-year-old. She began slowly but became more confident as she exercised her memory. She had seen these words before. The teacher should reinforce the 'sounding out' of the words by helping the pupil to 'hear' if she has chosen correctly. Sounding out and remembering must progress together.

MISSING MIDDLES 4

HOW TO MAKE THE GAME

○ Cut up the picture sheets to make small cards. Cut up all of the small vowel cards.

WHAT YOU NEED

○ A dice with four sides marked with a green spot and two sides marked with red ones.

○ A shaking cup.

HOW TO PLAY

○ Arrange the small vowel cards on the table in groups of the same sound, letter side up.

○ Give each player three picture cards and stack the rest.

○ Players take turn to shake the dice. If a green spot is thrown, the player may proceed to select one of the vowel cards to fit into one of his picture card spaces. If she chooses the correct vowel, she may keep the card and take another from the stack. If a red spot is thrown, the player must miss a turn. Continue till the cards are used up.

○ The players with the most completed words wins the game.

TEACHER GUIDANCE

This game may also be played putting the vowel cards into a feely bag and drawing from the bag in turn, instead of throwing the dice.

It gives additional practice in hearing and placing the vowel in three-letter words. The pupil has to look at her three words to see which vowel she needs to complete a word. She has to think it through and choose the right vowel by herself. The teacher needs to be quiet and patient while she does this; a lot can be learned by observing how she tackles the problem. If the pupil chooses a wrong vowel, ask "Why did you put 'a' in there?" Help her to be independent by correcting herself.

Sound out the whole word sometimes ("Well done, I'm glad you put 'i' in there to make 'p-i-g'."), especially if she is weak in her sounding of one or two letters. You can use the opportunity to reinforce them by repetition.

h _ n

b _ n

b _ _ d

b _ _ b

c _ t

c _ _ t

m __ g

m __ t

z __ p

b __ d

l __ g

b __ n

52

m _ p   c _ p   t _ p

v _ n   l _ d   l _ g

b__s   h__t   p__t

w__b   p__g   b__g

54

bus	a	e	i	o	u	a
hat	a	e	i	o	u	e
pot	a	e	i	o	u	i
web	a	e	i	o	u	o
pig	a	e	i	o	u	u
bag	a	e	i	o	u	a

mug	mat	zip
bed	log	bun
hen	bin	bud
bib	cot	cat
mop	cup	tap
van	lid	leg